The Collected
SECRET THOUGHTS

D1585640

THE COLLECTED
SECRET
THOUGHTS
OF

YOUR PHOTO HERE!

Steven Appleby

BLOOMSBURY

WITH MANY THANKS TO:
Polly, Liz, Noni, Matthew and ALL
at Bloomsbury...

First published 1996.
Paperback edition published 1997.
Copyright © Steven Appleby. 1996 & 1997.

The moral right of the author has been asserted.

BLOOMSBURY PUBLISHING PLC,
38 Soho Square, London W1V 5DF.

ISBN: 0 7475 3491 8

Printed in Great Britain by
St Edmundsbury Press, Suffolk.

This ~~book~~ CONTAINS
the SECRET THOUGHTS of:

MEN

WOMEN

CATS

BABIES

DOGS

& YOURSELF

The
SECRET
THOUGHTS
of
MEN

Grrrr...

AGE 20

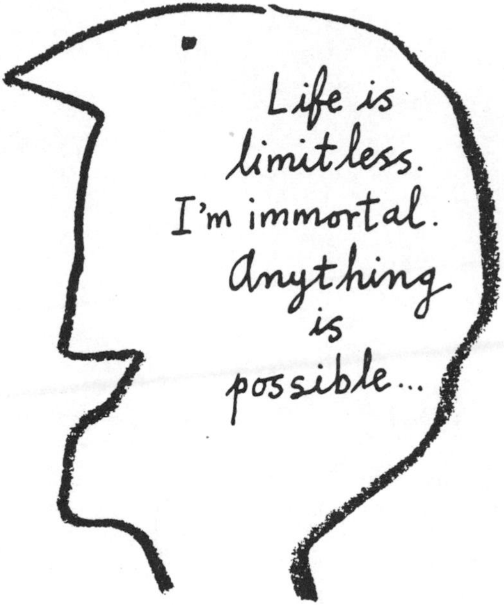

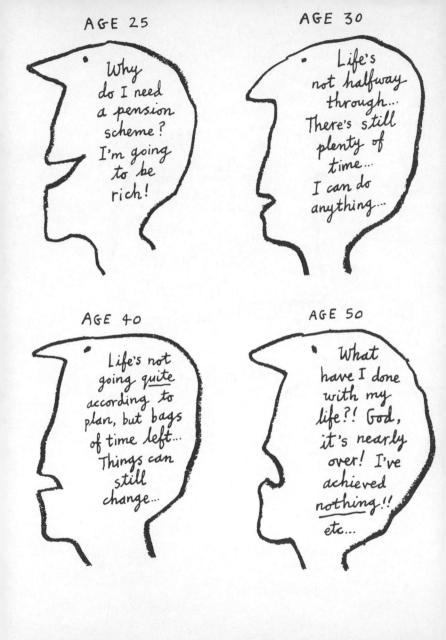

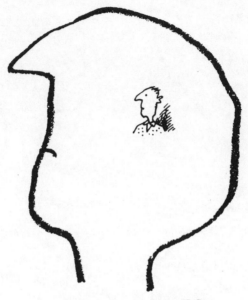

SMALL-MINDED

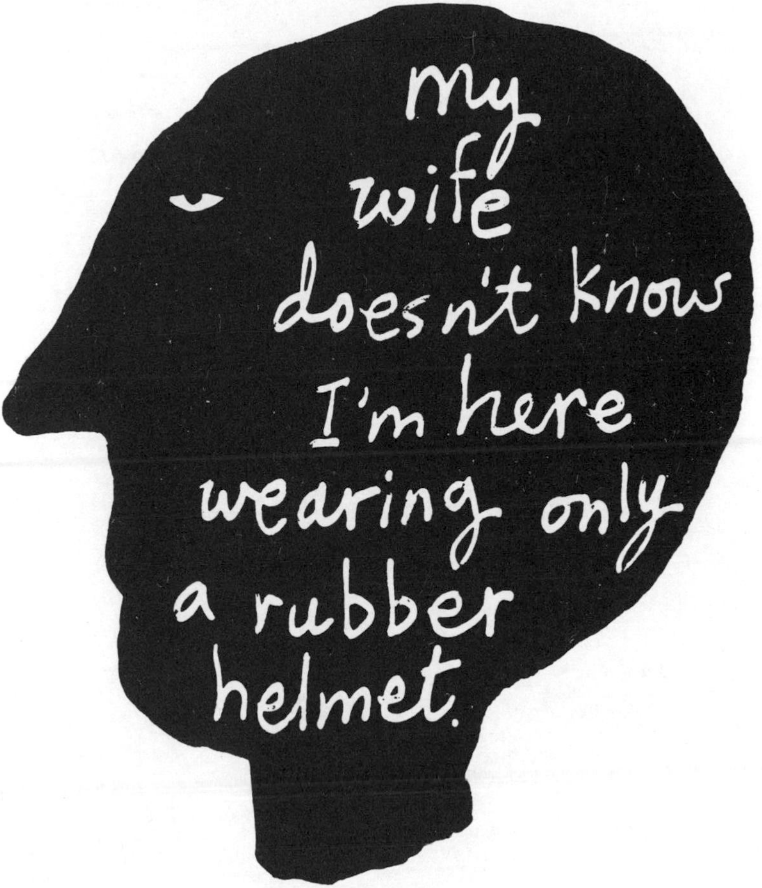
my
wife
doesn't know
I'm here
wearing only
a rubber
helmet.

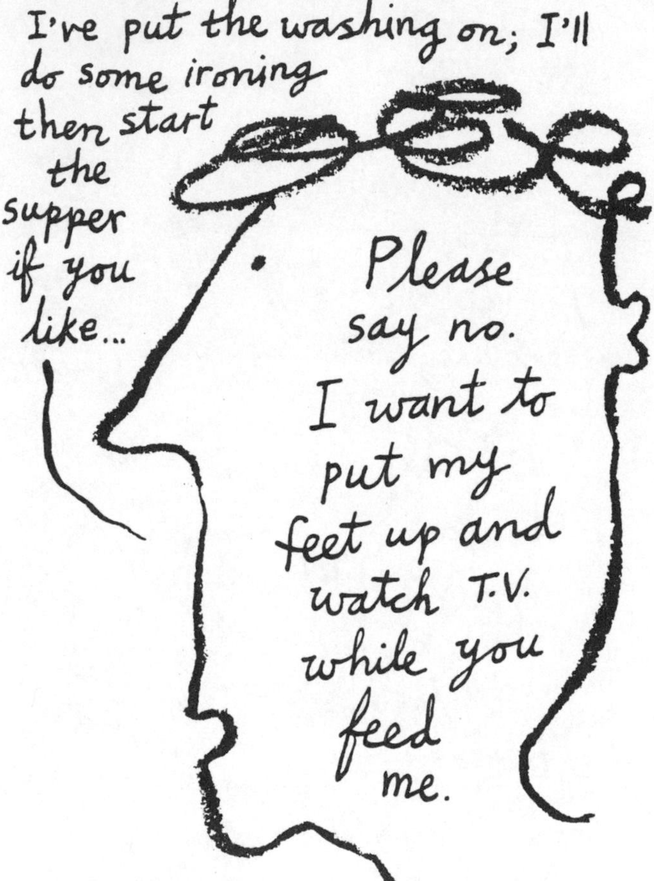
I've put the washing on; I'll do some ironing then start the supper if you like...
Please say no. I want to put my feet up and watch T.V. while you feed me.

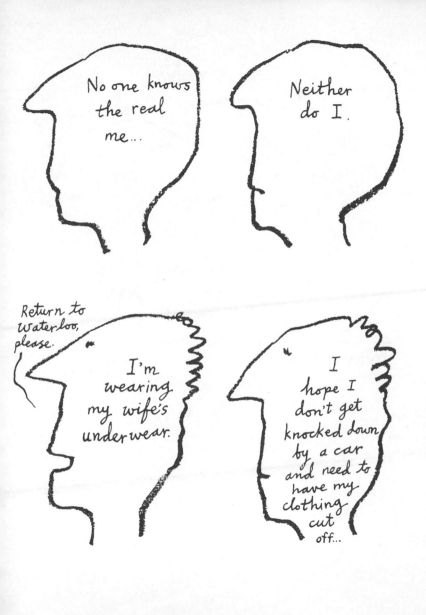

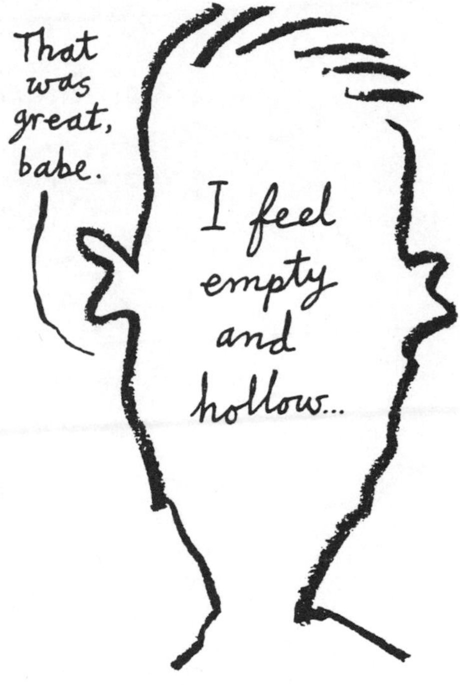
That was great, babe.
I feel empty and hollow...

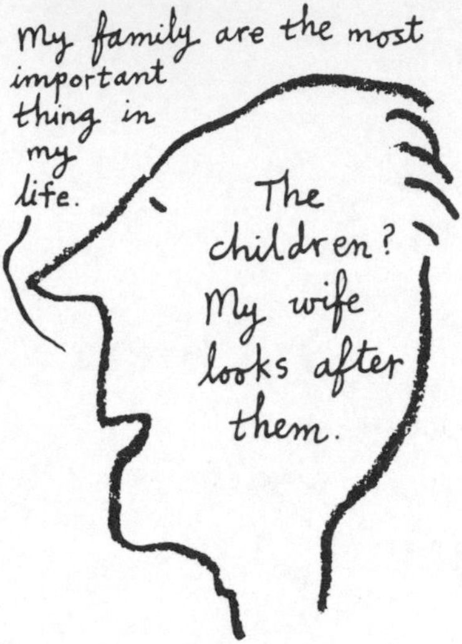

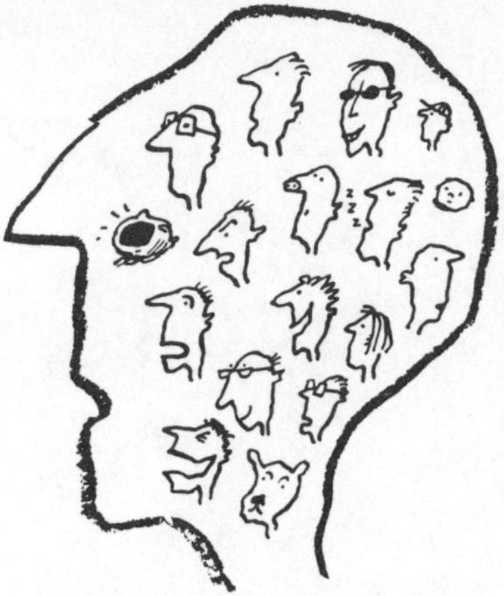

MULTIPLE PERSONALITY

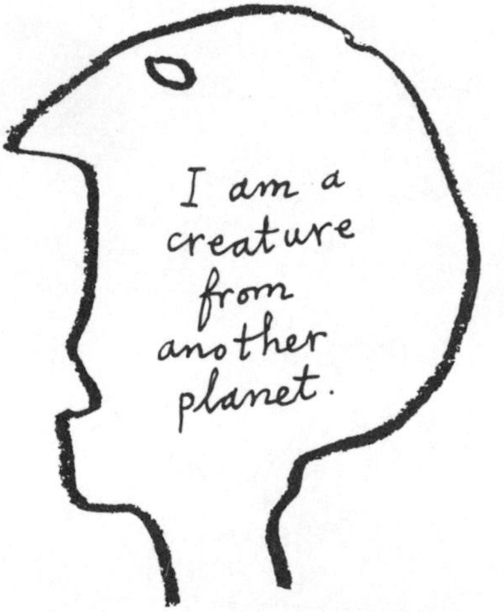

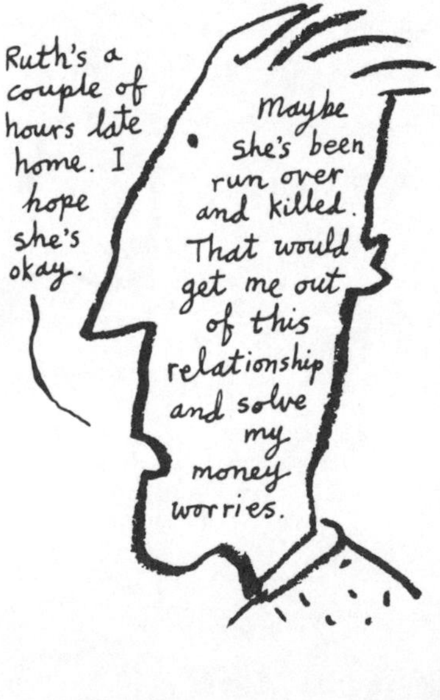

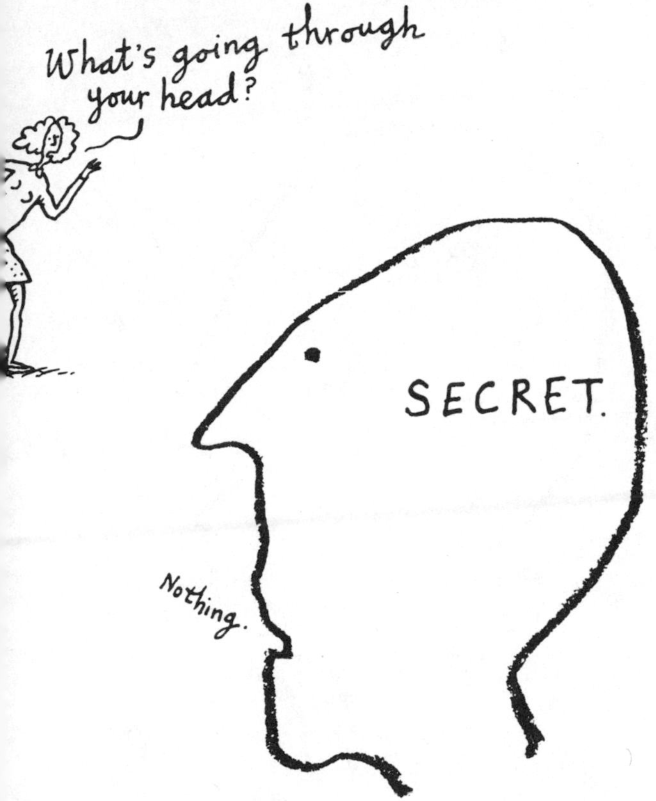
What's going through your head?
SECRET.
Nothing.

The
SECRET
THOUGHTS
of
WOMEN

W/up liquid.   Persil/Conditioner.
Choc!   toilet cleaner   Hoover bags
Sugar   tampons   bird seed
Bread   nappies   Bath sponge   cat food
butter/flour.   (cat litter? fore it.!!

crisps
cereals
baby food

champing...? te.

Veg:
t. carrots, peas
potatoes/new
leeks
tomatoes
lettuce
S.onions
cucumber

arsenic
sharp knives
polythene sheeting.
spade

NB.
recycle
— newspapers
— jars
— tins etc.
— cardboard

seed & plants.
Grass   assorted plants *
       MAKE
       * HAIR APPOINTMENT

NB. — Grass seed & plants.
       assorted plants

Get HOLIDAY BROCHURES!!
new suite.   — passport.
                  — travellers' cheque
fast car.
Clothes / suitcase(s)
Bikini   toothbrush

MANY THANKS TO:

Abigail; Gill; Janny;
Jean; Jessamy; Karen;
Kate; Linda; Liz;
Lorna; Mary; Nicola;
Noni; Rachel; Ros &
Sophie.

By the time I'm 30 I'll be married with a couple of kids.

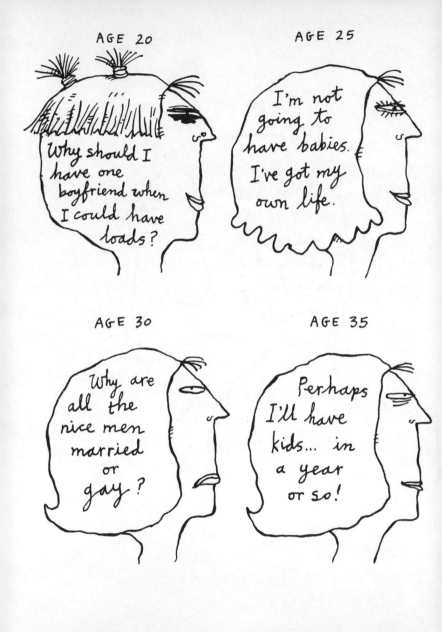

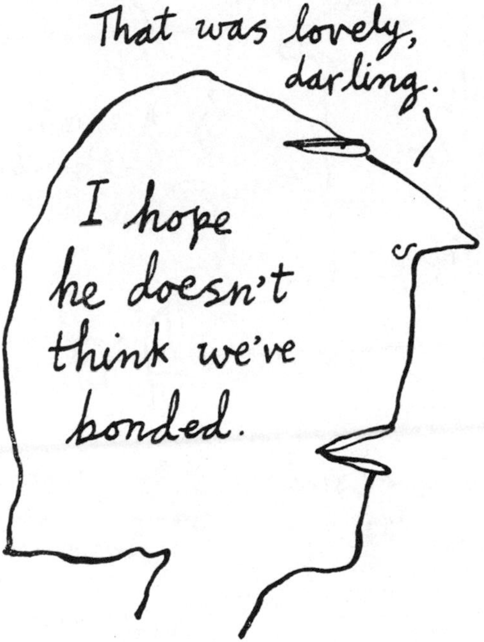
That was lovely, darling.
I hope he doesn't think we've bonded.

In memory of:
TERRY, DIBBLE, SALLY
& for JIM

The SECRET THOUGHTS of

CATS

a cat.

Incorporating

The INFINITE SUBTLETY of

CAT

EXPRESSIONS

Happy.

Sad.

Mildly
amused.

Pensive.

Just been
fed.

Waiting to
be fed.

Pleased.

Rather
cross.

Utterly
furious.

Slightly
irritated but
concealing it
well.

Staring at a
blank wall.

Sexually
aroused.

Not
interested.

Can't be
bothered.

About to kill
something.

About to do
nothing at all.

Suspicious...

Using the
cat tray.

Being watched
using the
cat tray.

Gloomy.

Bored.

Being
laughed at.

Worrying an
unintelligible
cat worry.

Asleep.

As good as
asleep.

Surprised.

Surprised but
pretending
not to be.

Gazing out of
the window.

Seeing something
exciting.

Purring.

Silent.

Not
thinking.

Thinking...

Thinking about
bottom licking.

Thinking about
nothing.

Sitting in a
cardboard box.

About to climb
inside a
carrier-bag.

Watching
invisible things.

Watching you
doing something
personal and
embarrassing.

Wondering if
there is a God.

Wondering what
was here before
the universe began.

Suspecting that
humans have
the ability to
read cat-thoughts.

Inscrutable.

Dead.

Afterthoughts...

If you put a piece
of paper, however
small, on the floor,
I will sit
on it.

I will touch an
outstretched pencil,
or finger, with
my nose.

My tongue
feels like
Velcro.

I have
unexplained
knobbly lumps
under my fur.

I live in 3 other
houses besides
yours.

I have 3 other
names, too.

We cats have
come here to take
over your planet,
earthling.

CAT HAIRS
ON CUSHIONS

FOR JASPER

The
SECRET THOUGHTS
of
BABIES

Waaaaaaaaaaaaa...

Steven Appleby

THE COMPLETE
NEW-BORN BABY
RANGE OF ACTIVITY:

Asleep.

Awake.

Eating.

Waaaaa...

Cross.

Not cross.
(NB – Babies are never
happy. Just not cross).

Filling a nappy.   Hungry.

Windy.

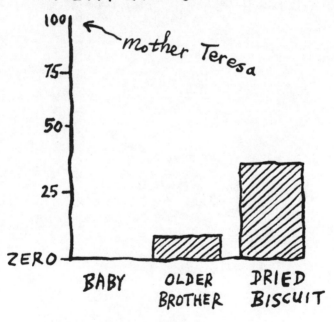

A BABY'S ABILITY TO EMPATHISE WITH OTHER LIVING CREATURES:

SOME ADVICE —
ALWAYS SUPPORT YOUR
BABY'S HEAD...

OR THIS WILL HAPPEN.

THOUGHTS AT 3 ~ 4 WEEKS

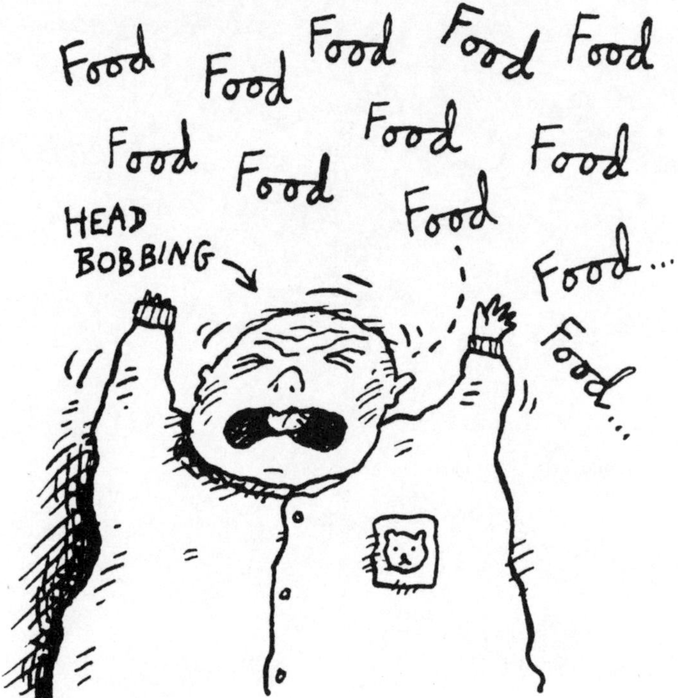

HOW BABIES SEE
THE WORLD

fig a ~

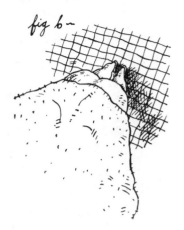

fig b ~

fig c ~

4 – 10 WEEKS

Confusion...
Surprise...
Puzzled...
Not understanding...
Perplexed...
Bewilderment...
Mixed up...
What's that?..
What's going on?...

THINGS THAT UPSET BABIES

Having their nappy changed.

Not having their nappy changed.

Being dressed.

Being undressed.

THINGS THAT MAKE
BABIES HAPPY...

Food.

Being asleep.

No clothes on at all.

SOME BABY THOUGHTS

"In a moment..."

"... for no particular reason, I am going to throw my arms and legs in the air and scream and scream and scream."

Waaaaa...

"I am doing this to drive you utterly crazy."

Waaaaa...

"I could stop at any time - if I wanted to."

Waaaaa...

"I'm unhappy so I want you to be unhappy too."

I'm testing you to see how much you love me."

"There's been a mistake! I'm not your baby! The hospital mixed up. Please send me home..."

I WON'T go to sleep!!"

"I won't go to sleep here..."

"or here..."

"or here..."

"or here..."

"or here..."

THEY GO TO SLEEP
IN AWKWARD PLACES.

THEY SLEEP _TOO_ QUIETLY...

AS SOON AS YOU'RE BUSY
THEY WAKE UP.

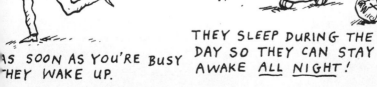

THEY SLEEP DURING THE
DAY SO THEY CAN STAY
AWAKE _ALL NIGHT_!

MUCH LATER...

MORE BABY THOUGHTS

"I have filled my nappy with green slime."

"The parent name I learn to say first is the one I love most"

*"Please answer this vital question which has been preying on my mind..."

*"Am I adopted?"

I am about to be sick."

"I LOVE this toy!"

Blu blu blu...

"It's my favourite..."

WAAH!

"Now I HATE it!!"

"Am I the Meaning
of Life?.."

BEFORE:

AFTER:

IT IS HARD TO BELIEVE,
BUT ONE DAY YOUR BABY
WILL GROW UP...

FoR Trudy, Bizzie, George, Dawn, Cassie, Johnny, Bella, mandy, Teddy Punch, Barney, Buster, Clipper, Patrick, Kelly, Sophie and all the others I haven't space to mention.

This looks like a good place to go to the toilet...

The
SECRET THOUGHTS
of
DOGS

Steven Appleby

The author, aged about two,
researching this book.

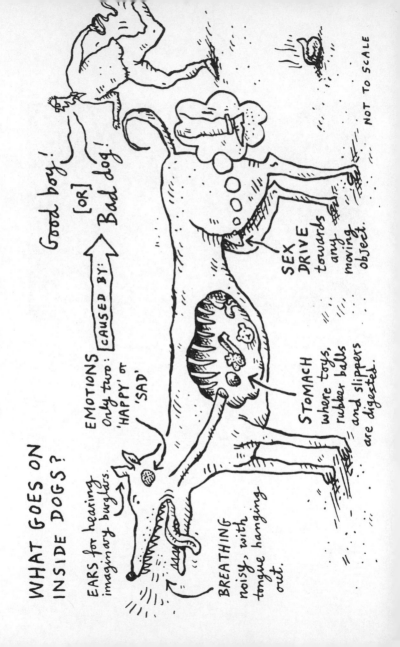

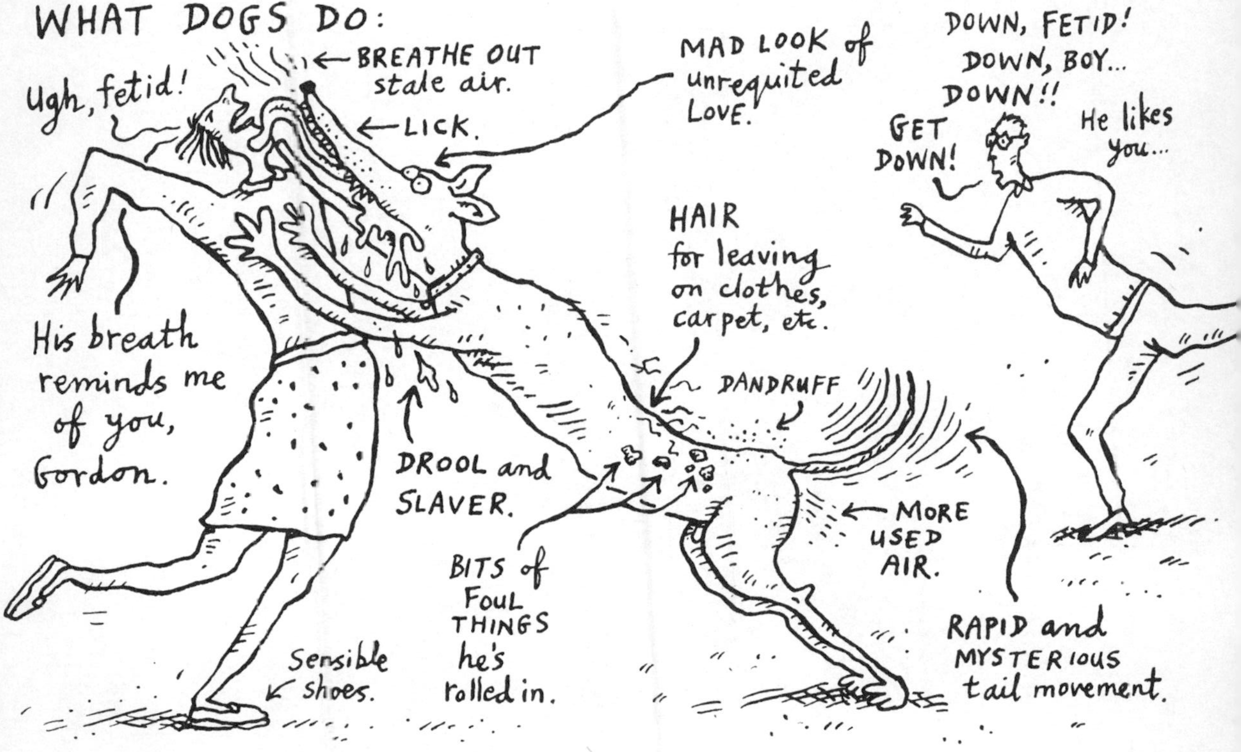
WHAT DOGS DO:
BREATHE OUT stale air.
Ugh, fetid!
LICK.
MAD LOOK of unrequited LOVE.
DOWN, FETID! DOWN, BOY... DOWN!!
GET DOWN!
He likes you...
His breath reminds me of you, Gordon.
HAIR for leaving on clothes, carpet, etc.
DANDRUFF
DROOL and SLAVER.
MORE USED AIR.
BITS of FOUL THINGS he's rolled in.
Sensible shoes.
RAPID and MYSTERIOUS tail movement.

MAIN PURPOSES
IN LIFE:

i – sleeping.

ii – Barking.

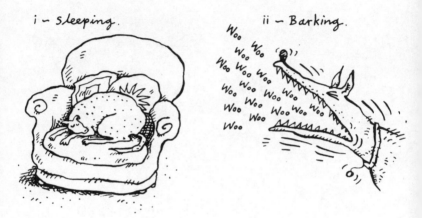

WHAT DOGS DO WHEN THERE'S SOMEONE AT THE DOOR...

i – Yourself.

ii – A complete stranger.

iii – An old family friend and frequent visitor.

iiii – A permanent member of the household.

v ~ Someone arriving at a house a few doors away.

vi ~ A sound inaudible to the human ear.

vii ~ A dangerous homicidal maniac.

viii ~ Burglars.

DOGS CAN LEARN LOTS OF THINGS!

"SIT!"   "FETCH!"

"LIE DOWN!"

"STAND UP!"

"WALK TO HEEL!"

"ROLL OVER."

"GIVE ME YOUR PAW!"

"BEG!"

"PLAY DEAD!"

"MAKE ME A CUP OF TEA, MILKY WITH TWO SUGARS!"

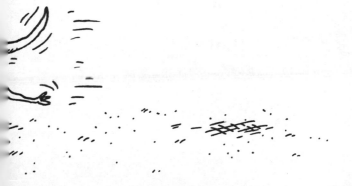

"I feel like running after a ball then bringing it back in return for some slivers of affection."
"You prostitute."

DOGS UNDERSTAND
EVERY WORD YOU SAY...

"I feel guilty because of your tone of voice. What did I do?"

"I feel happy because of your tone of voice. What did I do?"

"I feel chastened, then forgiven. We can start fresh as if it never happened... incidentally, what did I do?"

"I feel love, tempered by the tragic knowledge that we come from different worlds. It can never be. We must remain just friends, etc..."

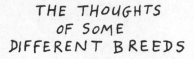

THE THOUGHTS
OF SOME
DIFFERENT BREEDS

WORDS TO SAY TO DOGS IN AN EXCITED TONE OF VOICE

SOME THOUGHTS
CONCERNING
FETCHING STICKS

"I shall pursue the stick and capture it!"

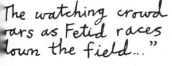

"The watching crowd roars as Fetid races down the field..."

"He feints... he turns... they're going crazy! Fetid pulls out his AK47..."

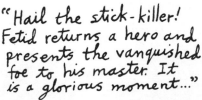

"rrowww wwl owrl budda budda budda budda keeeoooow!!"

"Hail the stick-killer! Fetid returns a hero and presents the vanquished foe to his master. It is a glorious moment..."

MORE THOUGHTS

"Gosh! You've got sexy legs..."

"When will I evolve hands?"

"Please put a toilet roll in your mouth and make a funny noise through it..."

"Yum! Boiled sheep's head and tripe with dry biscuit soaked in hot water... my favourite!"

"Just got to... aah...
break wind..."

"Sorry."

A THOUGHT MANY OWNERS HAVE:

MY
SECRET
THOUGHTS

by

— — — — — — —

— — — — — —

FRONTISPIECE

DEDICATION:

— — — — — — —
— — — — — — —
— — — — — — —
— — — — — — —

QUOTE *

--- --- --- --- --- --- --- ---
--- --- --- --- --- --- --- ---
--- --- --- --- --- --- --- ---
--- --- --- --- --- --- --- ---
--- --- --- --- --- --- --- ---

--- --- --- --- --- --- ---

* Taken from a favourite poem or book which sums up my life.

CONTENTS

BLANK
PAGE

FOREWORD

This fascinating book reveals absolutely EVERYTHING about _ _ _ _ _ _ _ _ _ in a quite startlingly honest way. Almost Sartre-esque, it draws upon _ _ _ _ _ _ _ _ _ _ _ 's personal traumas and experiences to paint a bare and utterly _ _ _ _ _ _ing portrait of someone at the _ _ _ _ _ _ _ of their life.

STEVEN APPLEBY

MY LIFE IN ALPHABETICAL
ORDER:

THE FRIENDS I DON'T
REALLY LIKE AT ALL:

THE FRIENDS I
ACTUALLY LIKE:

THE THINGS I LOOK FOR
IN A MEMBER OF THE
OPPOSITE SEX:

i — The correct private parts *

ii ~

iii ~

iv ~

v ~

vi ~

vii ~

viii ~

ix ~

JOIN THE DOTS TO REVEAL A
PORTRAIT OF YOUR OWN PSYCHE

* Delete if inapplicable.

SEXUAL EXPERIENCES
WHICH WERE INCREDIBLE:

DATE

SEXUAL EXPERIENCES
WHICH LEFT ME FEELING
HOLLOW AND DIRTY:

DATE

Continue on separate sheet if necessary...

MY AMBITIONS

MY SUCCESSES:

MY FAILURES:

ART THERAPY

GRAPH OF MY POPULARITY

DATE:
- - - - - - -

INTERCONNECTING BOXES:

No. of PHONE CALLS.

20
11
10
9
8
7
6
5
4
3
2
1
0

MON TUE WED THUR FRI SAT SUN

SELF-ANALYSIS

I am _ _ _ _ _ _ _ _ _

because _ _ _ _ _ _ _ _

_ _ _ _ _ _ _ _ _ _ _

Therefore I must be

a _ _ _ _ _ _ _ _ _ _

What I intend to do
to improve myself:

_ _ _ _ _ _ _ _ _ _

_ _ _ _ _ _ _ _ _ _

_ _ _ _ _ _ _ _ _ _

THE THINGS MY PARENT
DID WHICH FUCKED ME UP:

i ~

ii ~

iii ~

iv ~

v ~

vi ~

vii ~

viii ~

ix ~

Continue on separate sheet...

SIX DOODLES

NAMES and TELEPHONE
NUMBERS I want to forget: *

NAME   NUMBER

_____   _____
_____   _____
_____   _____
_____   _____
_____   _____
_____   _____
_____   _____
_____   _____

* Write them down then cross out.

PIE CHARTS

you
me

E CHART SHOWING HOW
NGRY I CAN GET

LOUR AS MANY SEGMENTS
AS NECESSARY)

PIE CHART SHOWING _ _ _ _
_ _ _ _ _ _ _ _ _ _ _ _ _

NOTE:
_ _ _ _ _ _ _ _ _ _ _ _ _

SHOULD I FINISH WITH
MY PARTNER ?

PROS	CONS
TOTAL:	

CONCLUSION: END RELATIONSHIP.
LIMP ON. *

* Delete as necessary.

PICTOGRAM OF THE KIND OF
SEX I LIKE BEST:

MY FANTASY:
(THE KIND OF SEX I THINK I
MIGHT LIKE BEST)

WHY I SHOULD KILL
MYSELF:

1 _ _ _ _ _ _ _ _ _
2 _ _ _ _ _ _ _ _ _
3 _ _ _ _ _ _ _ _ _
4 _ _ _ _ _ _ _ _ _
5 _ _ _ _ _ _ _ _ _
6 _ _ _ _ _ _ _ _ _
7 _ _ _ _ _ _ _ _ _

HOW IT RATED WHEN IT
ACTUALLY HAPPENED:
(1 - 10) [ ]

WHY I SHOULDN'T:

1 _ _ _ _ _ _ _ _ _

GUILT!
I feel guilty about...

PEOPLE TO TORTURE
HORRIBLY:

1 _ _ _ _ _ _ _ _ _

2 _ _ _ _ _ _ _ _ _

3 _ _ _ _ _ _ _ _ _

4 _ _ _ _ _ _ _ _ _

5 _ _ _ _ _ _ _ _ _

6 _ _ _ _ _ _ _ _ _

RESERVE:

_ _ _ _ _ _ _ _ _

SIX MORE DOODLES

AMBITIOUS DOODLE

I FEEL DEPRESSED TODAY.

- - - - - - - - - - -
           SIGNED

- - - - - - - - - - -
           DATE

MORE SELF-ANALYSIS

I hate _ _ _ _ _ _ _ _

because _ _ _ _ _ _ _ _

_ _ _ _ _ _ _ _ _ _ _

_ _ _ _ _ _ _ _ _ _ _

_ _ _ _ _ _ _ _ _ _ _

_ _ _ _ _ _ _ _ _ _ _

Therefore I am a _ _ _
person.

I will reap what I sow.

FEELING POSITIVE OR NEGATIVE

YES [   ] (TICK BOX)

NO [   ] ('X' BOX)

_ _ _ _ _ _ DATE

10 THINGS I CAN'T
STAND ABOUT
MY _ _ _ _ _ _ _ *

_ _ _ _ _   6
_ _ _ _ _ _ _ _ _

_ _ _ _ _   7
_ _ _ _ _ _ _ _ _

_ _ _ _ _   8
_ _ _ _ _ _ _ _ _

_ _ _ _ _   9
_ _ _ _ _ _ _ _ _

_ _ _ _ _   10
_ _ _ _ _ _ _ _ _

Partner; flatmate; best friend;
boss; life; self; etc.

MORE INTERCONNECTING BOXES

<u>SHOPPING LIST</u>

MY HOPES FOR THE
FUTURE:

_____
_____
_____
_____
_____
_____
_____
_____

FOOTNOTE: _____
_____

IMPORTANT THINGS I
MUST NOT FORGET!

AN OCCASIONAL DIARY

For recording momentous,
traumatic days only – ignore
days that are dull or merely
interesting.

DAY _ _ _ _ _ _ DATE _ _ _ _ _

Dear Diary,

_ _ _ _ _ _ _ _ _ _ _
_ _ _ _ _ _ _ _ _ _ _
_ _ _ _ _ _ _ _ _ _ _
_ _ _ _ _ _ _ _ _ _ _
_ _ _ _ _ _ _ _ _ _ _

- - - - - - -
- - - - - - -
- - - - - - -

Dear _ _ _ _ _ _ _ _

    I'm sorry I haven't been in touch for so long. I think of you often and intend to write, but never quite manage to put pen to paper. Well, here it is at last – a letter from me!

    Hope you are well.

    Very best wishes,

- - - - - - - - - -

Letter to tear out and leave unsent.

DAY _ _ _ _ _ DATE _ _ _ _ _.

Dear Diary,

DAY _ _ _ _ DATE _ _ _ _

Dear Diary,

DAY _ _ _ _ _ DATE _ _ _ _.

Dear Diary,

DAY _ _ _ _ _ DATE _ _ _

Dear Diary,

Y _ _ _ _ _ DATE _ _ _ _   DAY _ _ _ _ _ DATE _ _ _ _

_ar Diary,   Dear Diary,

_ _ _ _ _ _ _ _ _ _ _   _ _ _ _ _ _ _ _ _ _ _ _
_ _ _ _ _ _ _ _ _ _ _   _ _ _ _ _ _ _ _ _ _ _ _
_ _ _ _ _ _ _ _ _ _ _   _ _ _ _ _ _ _ _ _ _ _ _
_ _ _ _ _ _ _ _ _ _ _   _ _ _ _ _ _ _ _ _ _ _ _
_ _ _ _ _ _ _ _ _ _ _   _ _ _ _ _ _ _ _ _ _ _ _
_ _ _ _ _ _ _ _ _ _ _   _ _ _ _ _ _ _ _ _ _ _ _
_ _ _ _ _ _ _ _ _ _ _   _ _ _ _ _ _ _ _ _ _ _ _
_ _ _ _ _ _ _ _ _ _ _   _ _ _ _ _ _ _ _ _ _ _ _
_ _ _ _ _ _ _ _ _ _ _   _ _ _ _ _ _ _ _ _ _ _ _

        NOTES   NOTES

MY GROWING OLD CHECKLIST

FIRST ALCOHOLIC DRINK _ _ _ _ _ _.

FIRST CIGARETTE _ _ _ _ _ _ _ _ _

FIRST EXAM _ _ _ _ _ _ _ _ _ _ _

FIRST SEX _ _ _ _ _ _ _ _ _ _ _

FIRST JOB _ _ _ _ _ _ _ _ _ _ _

FIRST MARRIAGE _ _ _ _ _ _ _ _ _

FIRST GREY HAIR _ _ _ _ _ _ _ _

FIRST WRINKLES _ _ _ _ _ _ _ _

FIRST CHILD _ _ _ _ _ _ _ _ _

FIRST SENSIBLE CLOTHES _ _ _ _.

FIRST GROWN-UP HAIRCUT _ _ _ _

FIRST MEMORY LAPSE _ _ _ _ _

LAST CIGARETTE _ _ _ _ _ _ _.

OTHERS _ _ _ _ _ _ _ _ _ _ _

Thanks to _ _ _ _ _ _ _ _ _
_ _ _ _ _ _ _ _ _ _ _ _
_ _ _ _ _ _ _ _ _ _ _ _

END PAPERS

JOIN THE DOTS TO CREATE A
TRADITIONAL, MARBLED EFFECT